Doctoring, Better: 11 Top Physician Coaches Reveal Secrets for Helping Others Create Better Lives

Authors:

Foreword--C. Nicole Swiner, MD

Marjorie Stiegler , MD

Latanja Watkins, MD

Jattu Senesie, MD

Sheetal Ajmani, MD

Vanessa Jeffers, MD

Heather Hammerstedt, MD

Regina Allen Hardin, MD

Charmaine Gregory, MD

Maiysha Clairborne, MD

Sonia Wright, MD

ISBN: 978-1-7327525-9-7

FOREWORD: SUPER

Voted 1 of 10 Best Doctors in NC in 2017, C. Nicole Swiner, MD (DocSwiner) is a family physician, five-time best-selling author, blogger, speaker, wife and mother in Durham. She is also affectionately known as the Superwoman Complex expert and has written two best-selling books on the topic. She loves taking care of the family as a whole—from the cradle to the grave. Her interests include Minority Health, Women's Health, Self-Care and Entrepreneurship. She attended Duke University and went to medical school at the Medical University of South Carolina, in Charleston, SC. She's lived in the Triangle (Durham, NC) since finishing residency at UNC-Chapel Hill and continues teaching as an Adjunct Associate Professor with the Family Medicine department. When she's not treating patients at Durham Family Medicine, she's spending time with her family, planning items for her Superwomen subscription box program, speaking nationally, and teaching others to self-publish. Her passion is making medicine "plain" to her patients, so that all people, from all walks of life, can understand how to take better care of themselves and their families. She has become one of the nation's experts on self-care, physician burnout and well-being.

Welcome to *Doctoring, Better*! This is and has been a passion project of mine for the last couple of years. It seemed that there was confusion about what life and career coaches were, and since becoming one myself, I figured that I'd invite some of the most savvy and forward-thinking physicians to be a part of this book. And, here they are.

In this book, you'll find the answers you need for questions you have about your next step, career move or professional endeavor. We can and will help you to figure out what your greatest passion is in life and work and how to marry the two. Please feel free to lose yourself in their stories, and then reach out to them to schedule time to talk about what's most important to you. Each of their chapters begins with an action word that describes them and their approach to life and coaching, followed by their biographies.

I, in particular, am a specialist in publishing, hence the publishing and production of this collaborative book. Please reach out and let me know if you have that special work of art on your heart that you always wanted to publish and put out in the world. Swiner Publishing Company can help.

I also would love to help you figure out how to defeat the Superwoman complex, and find what businesses and career moves, both within and outside of medicine, are right for you. Coaching works!

So, dive in and take notes. We're here to help.

Love,

DocSwiner

TABLE OF CONTENTS

CHAPTER 1: SELF-LOVING

Dr. Sheetal Ajmani is a board-certified pediatrician, ayurveda lifestyle consultant, and yoga instructor. She helps busy professionals find inner peace through her coaching, online courses, and speaking events. www.sheetalajmani.com

I was lying on my back. On my yoga mat. At the local YMCA. Duane, the yoga teacher, was instructing the class to tense and release our muscles. He was leading us through a deep relaxation process, after which we'd lie in silence for a few minutes. It felt weird. But, I did it. And then, I experienced something I'd never known before. I experienced stillness. A peace within myself. I experienced a feeling of "witness." Of being present. I wasn't thinking about anatomy class, the exam I took earlier in the day, or my friends who were at happy hour.

It was my first year of medical school. I'd heard about this yoga thing but didn't know what it was. I was a runner. I figured yoga would be a good stretching routine to balance out my running. I knew yoga was from India, and so I was curious to learn more about this practice that came from my cultural roots. This curiosity, along with my girlfriends, led me to take my first yoga class at the YMCA. Little did I know that this curiosity would turn into a lifelong passion.

In yoga class, I tapped into a part of myself that I never knew existed. It was a space of stillness. Of "witnessing," rather than "doing." It was a space that I've come back to many times over the course of my medical career. A space that became my saving grace during the most difficult times of my career.

Internship was the most challenging year of my life. I felt alone. I felt inadequate. I felt sad. Like a true empath, I took on the emotions of my patients and their families. I was sensitive to the criticisms and harshness of my attendings. I was sleep-deprived and irritable. I didn't know how to leave work at the hospital. The heaviness of a child's death or sharing bad news with a family weighed on my soul long after I left the hospital.

I found myself on a challenging road of seeking and searching. I was seeking answers to questions like:

-Why do young children die? It's not fair!

-How do I tell parents that their child has a serious infection?

-How do I tell parents that I need to stick a needle in their newborn baby's back to collect cerebrospinal fluid?

- Where do I gather the strength to have those conversations and make those decisions?

-And, where do I turn after doing all that?

-Once I figure out how to have those conversations, how do I cope? Who do I talk to about it? Where can I go to process these experiences?

I knew I had to find some of those answers at the hospital. After all, that's where I was spending most of my time!

I recall an experience of being at a delivery in the middle of the night. While suctioning the baby's nose and figuring out her Apgar scores, I noticed her eyes open. In that moment, I realized that I was the first person she saw in this world. What a privilege and honor! In that moment, I shifted my focus to ***presence***. No longer thinking about how tired I felt or wondering if I'd see my call room that night. I was now grateful. Plain and simple. I felt grateful to be in my position. Grateful to witness such a magical moment. And, in that moment, I started a new tradition. I said to her and to every newborn baby I took care of since then, “Welcome to this world, dear soul. It’s a tough world out here, but it’s beautiful all the same. Enjoy it.”

I didn’t know it at the time, but I was practicing mindfulness. This was well before mindfulness became trendy! In fact, I’d never even heard the word “mindfulness.” I've come to learn that mindfulness is presence. It’s getting out of my head and noticing what’s around me. I’ve found the easiest way to find presence is through gratitude. Although it was hard at times, I realized that I could always find something to feel grateful for.

I also knew that I had to find solutions outside of the hospital. It wasn’t healthy for me to carry the burdens and sorrows of the hospital with me everywhere I went. I needed to create ***space*** to unload that weight. I found space through running, walking in Nature, and yoga. By creating this space for myself, I broadened my focus. In the hospital, I was laser focused. All that existed were my patients and me finding solutions. In Nature, I saw that my experiences in the hospital were one part of a much larger world. I was able to find peace in the room between my thoughts and experiences.

It was easy to get sucked into a state of negativity and cynicism with all that I saw in the hospital. Giving myself space helped me to see the beauty that exists in the world. Allowing myself to take in that perspective, allowed me to enter a flow state. It allowed me to let go of control, albeit temporarily (let's face it, letting go of control is hard for a type A perfectionist!). But space allowed for that shift in perspective.

So, remember I described myself as a type A perfectionist (correction: I'm now a *recovering* type A perfectionist!)? Well, that intensity, drive, and critical thinking led me to succeed. It's made me great at what I do. Great at passing exams, evaluating critical situations and making on-the-spot decisions. But, this same intensity, drive, and critical thinking when directed inwards was detrimental. How many times did I beat myself up with, "I should've done it this way instead. Why didn't I think of that? I should've known better!"?

Forgiving and being kind to myself is perhaps the hardest thing I've had to learn (and am still learning!). This is where the actions of ***love*** come in. I've trained for well over a decade on how to take care of patients. Through that entire process, there wasn't a single class on how to take care of myself. How to process the emotions of grief when a life was lost. How to communicate with sensitivity, while also monitoring the technical details of my patients' care. How to be whole in my career, relationships, and other interests.

This is where Ayurveda, a sister science to yoga, came in handy for me. Ayurveda is a system of lifestyle practices that promote wellness and joy. It wasn't until after residency that I discovered it. Ayurveda opened up a whole new way of looking at myself, my life, and my experiences. Through it, I came to understand my nature. Ayurveda says that I was born with a specific set of qualities that are completely unique. These qualities give rise to my interests and cravings. My constitution determines how I handle emotional stress. Ayurveda even talks about the type of schedule that's most balancing for my unique nature. Through it, I finally understood why it was so imbalancing for me to work 30-hour shifts with no sleep or consistent breaks for meals (I was lucky if I even ate dinner!). Through Ayurveda, I also learned a specific set of practices to live a whole life, one that honors all that I am. It was like a guide of self-care actions. I stumbled upon a blueprint of self-love specific to me! Just like I had to train to take care of others, I was finally training myself to take care of me!

Love brought me back full circle to that "witnessing" experience in my first yoga class. To seeing myself as the actor in the movie of my life. But I was also the person in the theater watching ("witnessing") the movie. As the actor, I was deep in it. It was hard to see the big picture. I was in the moment and reactive. Stepping out to be the person sitting in the movie theater, I was the witness. I knew the backstory and where the plot was heading. I could view it with perspective. And, I knew that no matter what happened in the movie, everything would be alright.

This perspective was ***grace.*** It was knowing that there was a greater power and purpose to everything I was experiencing. It was a practice of surrendering and letting go. A difficult practice, especially as a doctor. I like to be in control, so letting go was hard! Medical school trained me to be in control. That's the culture of medicine. I learned how to take control of situations. When a child in critical condition was rushed into the emergency room, I needed to jump into action. I was the actor. But, I was also able to watch from a distance as the viewer in the theater. I observed as life-saving measures were taken and then explained to the child's parents. As the witness, I saw the blood, sweat, and tears of the doctor who jumped in. No matter the result, I started to see every experience as part of the bigger picture of life. Where everything happened for a reason. I trusted that the same intelligence that kept life in balance in Nature was also working here in the hospital.

Through surrender, there's freedom. Let me clarify here. Surrender doesn't mean giving up. It means taking action from a place of doing your best while also realizing that there are higher forces at work.

Action from that place allows space for forgiveness, love, and compassion. It allows space for humanity. Humanity with ourselves, our patients, spouses, and children. We need to bring this humanity back. We need to start with ourselves first.

Through my journey, I discovered these 4 pillars – ***presence, space, love, and grace***. I've since built my life on these guiding principles. And, I help other physicians do the same. I help physicians like you find inner peace amidst the turmoil of our profession. I help you find greater life satisfaction and fulfillment. I help you understand your nature and how to optimize your strengths. I help you create a whole life, whatever that means for you. Most of all, I guide you to that place of knowing that you're worthy. Worthy of loving yourself, being loved, and creating the life of your dreams!

CHAPTER 2: LAYERED

Dr. Heather Hammerstedt is a nocturnist emergency physician, global health expert, smitten momma and wife, and lifestyle medicine physician who helps busy professional women finally break through the misconceptions around food, weight, exercise and mindset through lifestyle transformation coaching and consulting.

www.wholisthealth.com

One Emergency Department shift. One of nearly 1,980 shifts over the last 11 years as an attending emergency medicine physician. Why was it this shift that "shifted" me? It wasn't any different than any of the others, really. Motor vehicle crashes, myocardial infarctions, abdominal pain, migraines, back pain, a couple of code resuscitations and a gaggle of well kids with worried parents. In the midst of it all, I had a moment, where I saw the layers peel off of everything and everyone and SAW. Saw how much my colleagues were hurting and getting lost in themselves and the system. Saw how much my nurses were struggling with compassion fatigue and administrative overwhelm. Saw how confused my patients were on how to access care, who to trust for health information, how to wade through troughs of misinformation. How everyone was overweight, undervalued, overwhelmed, heading to dis-ease in their mental and physical futures. Everyone laid bare. It was an astounding moment, and one that changed the trajectory of my career and my service to others. Someone has to do something about this, clear up the mass confusion, lead people to value themselves and their bodies, advocate for patients and for physicians. If not me, who?

With each interaction, I was suddenly able to peel beyond the current reality to the possible root causes. The patient who comes to the ED with chest pain, it's not just "is it an MI or not?". Peel off the anxiety, peel off the sugary processed food, peel off the hidden hangover, peel off the skipped exercise, peel off the stress of a sick parent, peel off the child with the behavioral problem, peel off the "I'm not enough". The consultant physician who yells over the phone about being called for his expertise. Peel off the lack of sleep, peel off the stress of an independent business, peel off the lack of nutrients in a packed OR day, peel off the understaffed surgical floor, peel off yesterday's complication, peel off the stressed marriage, peel off the malignant residency experience, peel off the frustration of "just one more thing", peel off the pizza and pasta and caffeinated soda all eaten in the hallway. The nurse who can't help roll a patient because she is now nearing 300bs. Peel off the understaffed schedule, peel off no lunch break, peel off 12 hour days that become 14 hour days, peel off the adult child and the elderly parent in her house, peel off the ease of grabbing packages to eat, peel off the "I'm not valuable," peel off the "I'm too tired to go on a walk," peel off the "everyone needs me," peel off the exhaustion. The patient who is standing at the nurse's station, pounding his hands in anger, red-faced. Peel off the fear, peel off the sugared coffee and donut as breakfast, peel off the childhood violence, peel off the stressful graveyard job, peel off the bills, peel off the last healthcare experience, peel off the being 'unheard,' peel off the black and white.

I looked back on my experiences, my years of "hands up" for knowledge, over my years. Integrative nutrition health coaching course, medical acupuncture course, six months in India studying Ayurveda, a decade of work in East Africa, a decade of emergency medicine clinical practice and administrative work, five years in legislative advocacy, study of ahimsa in Buddhism, a second board certification in lifestyle medicine. When it came down to it, it all suddenly was weaving itself together, I was seeing the trees and the forest, and I could see that the healthcare system was broken and that a new way was necessary, for both the physicians and the patients.

I saw the solution: it's transparency, it's kindness, it's openness, it's seeing the humanity in us all, it's digging through the layers to find the root of Value in each person, getting them to see their own Value, and to start treating themselves as they deserve to be treated at the most basic level. Providing them with the evidence and education on how and with what they should be treating themselves. Giving themselves the opportunity to see themselves, create choices that serve them and get them the results they want. You can't help others in health care if you can't help yourself, and you can't receive care if you don't see yourself yet or if you're in a system that doesn't see you. This isn't something we can do well in conventional medicine, where we are prescriptive, paternalistic, and in a seat of power trying to "solve" the problems of others with a keystroke. In a coaching model, like lifestyle medicine utilizes, those layers can be exposed, the root opened, and the space held for people to find their truth. Resolving discrepancy between what someone wants and what they do is only possible when that space is held with authenticity and trust.

It's interesting that the first things that people lose when they stop valuing themselves is what they eat, how they sleep and how they move their body. Creating a healthy present and a healthy future means that we each- the patient, the nurse, the doctor- need to put our basic layers in order, to build on that strong foundation. Whole unprocessed foods, balanced exercise, mindfulness meditation, quality sleep, and honestly knowing yourself form that core layer. When someone is 'feeding' that core, she is able to fill her cup and then is able to fill others. Not to mention, the weight improves, the mood improves, the cognitive agility improves, the physical health improves.

Living and learning lifestyle medicine, using food and sleep and exercise and mindset as medicine, has drastically altered my ability to care for myself, my patients and my family, and changed my path in life and career. I'm rededicated to my role as a physician (and coach) in a new way: improving the Health IQ of my community, whether that is social media education and podcasting to the public, consulting on wellness to companies, coaching my private clients, teaching other physicians the evidence behind lifestyle change for prevention of disease, or working on 'seeing' my patients and colleagues where they are and speaking to that. I've even found ways to sneak in food and exercise prescriptions to my EMR discharge paperwork in the emergency department, as often I find patients ready to hear and implement change during and after a perceived (or real) emergency, and often two minutes is all it takes. My private clients receive personalized telehealth coaching on food, weight, exercise, mindfulness and daily podcast information on weight science and mindset around food digitally delivered to them, so that they not only have the support and accountability, but also the evidence and education to empower them for sustainable lifestyle change toward prevention and reversal of disease and to be a force of education and care for others in the same light. My professional satisfaction has skyrocketed, I'm serving people at their most basal needs and creating futures for them that they deserve, and curating physicians who can truly revolutionize the way we provide care.

I'm heading to an ED shift tonight, and I'll see all of those layers all over again, in every person, once seen it is hard to unsee. But this time, I won't have the same anguish, instead I'll feel hope and hopefulness, because once seen, those layers become modifiable. Modifiable means progress toward a whole, healthy mind and body and community, and a "healthier" healthcare system.

CHAPTER 3: DISRUPTIVE

Dr. Maiysha Clairborne. Board Certified Family Physician, Business & Entrepreneur Coach, & Founder of Stress Free Mom MD & The Next Level Physicians Entrepreneur Institute. She helps physicians find their passion and then systematically turn that passion into a profitable business that leverages their time, doing what they love and practicing on their own terms.

(Taking the Road Most Doctors Forget About: The Road of Passion & Purpose)

I'm the oldest of 7 kids. Grew up with 2 younger sisters. My mom was a dentist, and my dad was a doctor, so I think I was destined to be on this path. My mom was my first coach. She showed me that against all odds, success was possible. I'd like to say my parents were the inspiration for me being a doctor, but they weren't...at least not consciously. I actually decided I wanted to be a doctor from an 8th grade college writing assignment. Random I know, but it's true. I was sitting there in class, looking through the college directory, and the thought occurred to me "I think I'll be a doctor" ... and that was that.

Once I set my mind to something, there's no telling me it can't be done.

So, fast forward... Undergrad... Med School, and then there was that glorious moment when I got those two letters behind my name...you know what I'm talking about right? M.D. For some of you it's DO or DDS, maybe ND or DC even. It was a proud time. Then came residency. You know how you suddenly realize that you have gotten yourself into something you didn't realize you had signed up for? That was my residency experience.

I remember so clearly how that first experience of burnout almost took my life. And my first experience of what I now know to be burnout was in residency, but back then there was no language for it. I knew something was wrong, because I had this thought about 6 months into my intern year, "what did I get myself into...I did not sign up for this". But the reality for me was that I was in too deep to quit (and besides doctors don't quit.... and we'll talk about that later) ... and an added layer for me: strong black women don't quit. So, I kept pushing, and I noticed myself get more numb, more disconnected, sad. Soon, sadness turned to depression, but I kept pushing until I found myself one night post-call staring down the barrel of a bottle of Percocet that I had from a knee surgery a few months ago, thinking "I can't go on like this" I picked up that bottle...I opened it and stared at those pills.. and somehow, I had a moment of clarity: I was not going out like this, and I picked up the phone, called a girlfriend: voicemail. In a panic I called another friend, and no one was answering so I dropped to my knees and asked God to please give me the strength to live through the night... Now, I write poetry, and that night writing saved my life. I picked up my pen, opened my journal and through tears I wrote...and wrote and wrote...and the next morning I awoke to find that I had survived the night, literally writing myself to sleep. The next day I got help, but that was a defining moment for me: the moment I knew that I could not go on practicing like the factory worker they were training me to be, blindly following orders while completely ignoring what mattered to me. I was lucky, I survived, but my classmate Monty didn't survive. My classmate Sophia didn't survive...

As I went through the rest of my residency, I spent a lot of time thinking about what it was that I wanted to do. I always loved the "holistic style" of practice, so I decided I'd pursue that. And straight out of residency, with blind optimism, decided I would start my own practice. The problem was that I had no knowledge of business, or marketing, and had no idea how to set up a practice. Still I jumped in anyway and guess what? I failed... flat on my face! Within 6 months of opening, I closed.

For me, that was only motivation to discover what was missing. And so I spent the next 3 years studying, learning practice styles, business, and marketing. I used locums as a strategy to look under the hood of other practices. I got coaches and mentors for marketing, business, and sales. And in 2007, I jumped in again. I started a cash-based "holistic style" practice with no patient base, and less than $1000 in the bank RIGHT before the recession hit. And I grew it successfully in spite of that recession. But it wasn't long before I'd begin to feel that spiral again.

So, there I was, in this concierge style practice doing well, but feeling...well... bored, empty...like "is this it?" But I was comfortable though. I was doing well. I didn't dislike what I was doing. But I was no longer lit up. I added on more services, got more trainings to spice things up but kept coming back to the same place of "I'm just not feeling like this is it". I was beginning to dread going into the office. I kept feeling like... "there's got to be something more..."

All I wanted was to build a successful practice, doing what I loved and making a difference in healing and empowering others. And it seemed like I had created that very thing. But I still was not completely happy. I felt like I was still trapped in this traditional model of being a doctor.

The truth is, all my life I had been doing what was expected of me, what I was supposed to. I had been the A student, graduated top of my class in med school, high performing in residency. I had been doing "everything right" looking like I had it all together. I had even built what my colleagues would consider "the cush life" but I wasn't happy. I was still struggling with who I was, with what difference I was really making, with what I was really put on this earth to do. I didn't feel like my contribution really mattered. I didn't really feel like I mattered.

Then one day, I'm in this communication seminar, and I'm talking about my feeling like I'm burning out even in this "cush-feeling job" because I'm not making the biggest difference I could make and she says to me, "You are not alone." "I am not alone." The words rolled around in my head for a moment, and then it hit me: "OMG! I am NOT alone. What if other doctors are feeling this way too? I've got the skills, the proven results from coaching patients, and this CERTAINLY would be making a bigger difference!" That is when I decided to shift my focus to coaching physicians. It started with burnout. I had experienced it twice (by now) and had recovered from it twice. Very quickly, I began to be pulled in the direction of helping physicians find and create their ideal careers in clinical medicine because much of what I was finding was that the docs who came to me were burned out because they had just "fallen into" their jobs or careers rather than chosen them (and I'm all about choice). Then I began to attract physicians who were ready to leave medicine altogether. Since I had basically done just that, it was a natural pivot into helping physicians discover their passion and then create their careers in line with that. I had become the physician who made creating a dream career possible.

Two years later, I wake up every morning realizing that I have found my true passion, my calling, my purpose. Not only do I LOVE coaching doctors, I LOVE helping them create breakthrough results in their lives, realize their passion, and create whole profitable businesses out of that passion. "Ikigai". That is the Japanese word for purpose. It's when your passion, mission, profession, and vocation come together in perfect harmony. I found mine and my passion and purpose are helping other doctors find theirs.

After a long journey, I finally feel like I am making a

REAL difference. That I am creating a legacy for my colleagues, for future doctors and the future of the industry. More so, I finally know who I am. I finally see myself as the kind of leader who creates transformation and I get to be a part of a revolutionary movement in our industry.

What I want you to be left with is that it IS possible to create a career that combines what you are an expert in (your profession), What you love (your passion), and What you stand for (and what the world needs) into something that you can be well-compensated for. This is the path I lead doctors on every day.

CHAPTER 4: EFFECTIVE

Dr. LaTanja Watkins is a certified life coach, author, and speaker who is board certified in both Anatomic Pathology and Forensic Pathology. She was inspired to become The Physician Burnout Coach™ in order to help physicians finally enjoy the life they have worked so hard to create.

You have invested hundreds of thousands of dollars, your youth, and many priceless holidays, birthdays and/or family vacations in order to become a doctor—all of which is pointless if you don't bother to invest in your own well-being. You've been taught your entire life that once you have "made it," life will be amazing, but no one ever told you about the chronic stress that comes along with being a medical doctor and how, if you let it, it will destroy you. The point is that you want to enjoy the life that you have worked so hard to create. So why does it feel so unfulfilling at times? And, if you are anything like I was, why do you constantly daydream of quitting?

I know you want to help people. I know in the beginning you saw yourself providing excellent patient care and giving back to the medical profession in the form of teaching, mentorship, or making contributions to your field as a thought leader. Yet, somewhere along the way things shifted and your life does not look anything like you initially imagined. You have spent years "gutting it out" and working extremely hard to get to where you are in your career. Now, you just want to be highly productive and focused at work and still have the energy to have that same level of focus for yourself and your family when you get home without feeling exhausted and overextended. But more than anything else, you really want to finally feel settled so that you can enjoy the life you have worked so hard to create, right? For many of us, this leads to the question of: What does this look like?

As The Physician Burnout Coach™ I coach physicians just like you and help them navigate the waters of chronic stress, burnout, being overwhelmed, the growing desire to quit, and/or coping with the general feeling that there's just something missing. Believe me, I feel as if I already know you pretty well because these are the same waters, I had to navigate for myself. You may feel as if you have all of the responsibility, but no power when it comes to work. Your workday is the alpha and the omega meaning that it pretty much never ends. From the moment you start thinking about work, you are "on." When you are at work, you are so engrossed in caring for your patients or handling logistics that you often forget to take even a short lunch break for yourself or you may even choose not to eat at all.

When you finally do decide to call it a day, you are using your "free" time either thinking about work or completing the work you brought home with you. Does this sound familiar? You may even spend a lot of time feeling anxious or worrying that you may have done something wrong, or that you have forgotten something. Worse of all, thoughts may linger as to whether or not you have screwed something up. All too many of us still wonder when "they" will figure out that they made a mistake by even giving us a medical degree in the first place. Some refer to this as the imposter syndrome.

Yet, this doesn't just revolve around work; it can seep into our home lives as well. You may also be short tempered with your kids and your spouse more often than you would like to admit and your kids may have even started drawing family pictures without you in them. You are exhausted and worn out. Yet, as tired as you are, you're not even sleeping. At times, you resent having chosen medicine as a career; you consistently daydream and plot about quitting. Let's be honest, there aren't enough wine flights, international trips, shopping sprees, or James Beard award-winning restaurants that can help you hide anymore.

If this sounds like you, you are in the right place! In fact, this is essentially the "before" story for most of the physicians who I coach, including myself. My own trajectory as an overworked and overwhelmed doctor is what led me to hiring my first life coach.

There comes a point when you realize that you have gotten so used to prioritizing your career and your patients over your own health and well-being that you know it is time to make a change. When so much of your adult life has been spent striving and jumping through all sorts of massive hoops with tremendous dedication in order to just make it through training, you can get lost in the paradigm. All the time you were thinking (or at least hoping) that things would get better once you completed your medical training, but did they?

One day, you realize things don't really get that much better; there are always more hoops, and that there is the unspoken expectation that you should continue in this unhealthy pattern for an additional 30 or so years and then you can finally retire and enjoy the rest of your life. How many years of life will that leave you with and what quality of life will you have—not to mention that you will only reach this provided that you don't pass away at work clicking through electronic health records seething over why it takes what feels like an entire lunch break just to get to the next screen (Arrgh!).

Then, like a lightning bolt, it finally hits you that the same dedication and grit that got you through your training is starting to consume you and it is affecting other areas in your life outside of work. You may overcompensate by spending way too much money; your relationships may become challenged; and your new best friends go by the names of Ms. Wine (red please!) and Mr. Taco. There is no way you can keep this up for the next 2 years, let alone the next 30!

It becomes glaringly clear that you can no longer continue to "do whatever it takes" to meet the expectations of the medical field. You have already been doing that for so long, even to the detriment of your own body's basic needs like quality nourishment and a good night's rest. Living on pure adrenaline has depleted your vital energy storage and you have been foregoing proper rest and relaxation for years. Finally, you realize that this part of your life does not feel like success at all.

As medical doctors, we were REALLY committed to getting to where we are in our careers. And quite frankly, a lot of us spend more time with our jobs and in our careers (or thinking about them) than we will ever spend with the people who we proclaim to love the most. Out of 168 hours in a week, we spend on average 4.5 hours commuting to and from work. We spend on average 30 minutes getting ready for work which equals 2.5 hours, at least, per week. If you are one of the extremely fortunate physicians, you spend 8 hours a day actually at work without having to take any additional work home with you. This leads to 56 hours for sleep. If you add in a 24 hour call for many of my physician friends on any given week, then there are 49 hours left in the week that you now have to split between significant others, kids, other obligations, self-care, and any other hopes and dreams that you have or may have once had. 1/3 of our life is spent at work, 1/3 of our life asleep, and the last 1/3 has you feeling like you are being grabbed at from every direction with life's demands, expectations, and responsibilities. It is no wonder that there is such an epidemic of burnout and chronic stress in our profession!

Don't get me wrong. At times, stress is necessary. If I were ever to end up on an operating table, I want my surgeon to feel the stress of keeping me alive. People who go the ER with a gunshot wound or symptoms of a heart attack need their doctors to be able to effectively deal with the stressors of the moment and do all that they can so that their patient hopefully does not succumb to any unnecessary morbidity and/or mortality. Stress is your reaction to the challenges and demands that present themselves to you. When appropriate, and of limited duration, it can be a good thing.

In short bursts, stress can be positive, such as when it helps you avoid danger or meet a deadline or when you use it to keep your patient alive. Without the stress of overcoming challenges, changes, and hardships in our lives, we would not grow to develop the resilience or "grit" that makes us so valuable. We would not learn to be resourceful. We are doctors. We are some of the smartest, strongest, and most resourceful people on the planet. Yet, we have never been taught to take care of ourselves.

And what's funny about medicine, the healing profession, is that you learn somewhere along the way that these sacrifices just come along with the territory of being a doctor. You are taught that you are more of a superhuman than other humans and that the personality of a true doctor is one that can handle and survive these superhuman expectations—forever. We are usually seen as the epitome of healers, but how effective can we truly operate in our gifts if we don't even know how to begin to heal ourselves?

Everywhere you look, you hear calls for solutions to physician burnout because it has been reported that over one-half of physicians in the United States experience symptoms of burnout. This, in turn, leads to doctors leaving medicine for other careers as well as suboptimal patient care. Imagine if one-half of all doctors in the country quit tomorrow or if you made a preventable, fatal mistake because you did not know how to effectively manage burnout. Think about failing your $2000 board examination or recertification for the third time and not understanding why. Let that sink in for a moment. The stakes are high. Burnout also often leads to strained relationships, escapist behaviors (binge-drinking anyone?), and yes, self-harm. Not taking care of yourself at the expense of work and other obligations is a form of self-harm. Just as we took an oath to "do no harm" to others, we must also apply this to our own lives.

It is wonderful that physician issues are appearing to finally be taken seriously. Yet, for all of the talk about burnout and the solutions offered to solve it, there is one thing still missing—effectiveness. Most solutions are action oriented with encouragement for changing the system which isn't going anywhere anytime soon. Other solutions hone in on changing the physician; there is nothing wrong with you except that you are not an X-man superhuman. You just haven't learned effective strategies that help you to manage the reasons why you are experiencing burnout in the first place. And that is what I have taught myself and what I teach to all of my clients. I teach you what you should have learned in medical school, but never did. I teach you how not to quit just because you feel like you "just can't keep doing this" (at least not right now). What most people do not realize is that quitting one thing in a state of frustration will only lead to more frustration down the road because you never addressed the root of your frustration in the first place...and wherever you go, there you are. My clients learn to rekindle their relationship with medicine by focusing on and processing how they manage and think about their relationship with work. This is critically important because it will affect every other relationship in your life. It will affect how you show up for yourself and the people you love, which will result in greater awareness, healthier relationships, and a happier, more fulfilling life. You have worked extremely hard for this life. You deserve to enjoy it. Time is your most valuable commodity. Do not waste another day hoping things will get better. We both know nothing ever changes that way. Decide that things are going to get better now.

I would love to help you. I offer a limited number of FREE consultations per week on a first come, first served basis. The session is 45-minutes in which I will help you discover an effective solution for the one area in which burnout affects you most. It will transform your life. Go to https://latanjawatkins.com to schedule now! Just click the black button that says "book your free discovery session here.

CHAPTER 5: FEARLESS

Dr. Charmaine Gregory is a wife, mom of three cherubs and a night shift Emergency Physician who is passionate about fitness and health. As a survivor of burnout who used self-care as a pathway to recovery, she helps women reclaim their wellness mojo through fitness, nutrition, life and leadership coaching.

Fearlessness is not the absence of fear but instead the ability to convert the negative energy of fear into positive and liberating fuel for success. This concept encapsulates my philosophy of coaching. As a coach, my objective is to stir up momentum in my clients that may have been dormant or untapped.

When interviewed, top performers say that coaching helped them be their best. If you think about a time when you were pushed to be better, then that was also a time when you were being coached. I grew up in Jamaica, West Indies, and New York City; throughout my childhood, I have had coaches. For sports. For academics. For dance. For drama. For leadership.

It seemed as though as I progressed through college and medical school, that coaching was less and less accessible. These were the times that it was most needed. Despite this, life pressed on and I had to face several fears head-on. As I reflect on some of the setbacks I had in medical school, I cannot say that I was going through a tough time with family, health or having significant situational stress, yet I found myself facing a failing grade on the USMLE (United States Medical Licensing Exam) Step 1. This was a time that I questioned my ability to continue in the study of medicine, my self-worth, and my intellect. Not passing was very significant indeed. It meant that I was not allowed to start clinical rotations until successfully retaking the exam.

So, a little back story may be helpful here. When I was 8 years old, I declared to my mother that I wanted to be a physician. I had no family or friends that were in the medical field. My only contact with medicine was my Pediatrician, who I loved to see because it meant I might get a shot (strange, I know).

At this time, we were still living in Jamaica. My mom looked at the options, one medical school on the island and competition from the best and brightest not only in Jamaica but also the rest of the Caribbean and heavy competition to get into a great high school and made the decision to leave for the United States. Talk about faith and stepping out despite fear! There were a lot of sacrifices that led up to my seat in the medical school class. I was the first to go to college in my family. I was the first to pursue post-graduate education. The legacy of my family was at stake and I had failed my mother who sacrificed her lifestyle to start over in a new country solely based on the spoken dream born in an 8-year-old mind. I had failed myself. Boy, could I have used a coach at this point in my life!

Like every storm, there is a rainbow that appears when it is over. My rainbow took the form of a passing score on my retake. The blemish on my record haunted me still and reared its ugly head when it came time for applying to residency. Fear played a record in my mind that the odds were not in my favor, but something within pushed me to apply to as many programs as I could afford and put my best foot forward on the interview trail. Let's just say that my heart was in my throat the entire day the Monday of match week. Thankfully, everything worked out and I matched where I needed to be and got amazing training in Emergency Medicine.

Let's fast forward to the end of my residency. I fell in love with an amazing man who happened to live in Michigan, and he was established in his career with a positive trajectory. So, the geography of my job search was limited. There was intense fear during this time related to not being able to find work and make a meaningful financial contribution to my new family. Fear became fuel and I put myself out there, interviewed and thankfully got a position in what was then a tight market.

There I was, 30 years old, a brand new Emergency Medicine attending doctor living the dream that was born in my 8-year-old mind! I was on fire! I started to search for my niche by saying "yes" to every and all opportunities in the hope that my niche would become clear. It was the best of worlds, I was seeing patients, teaching residents and students and being a healer like I aspired to be. As my career progressed forward, life was progressing as well. Our family grew and we had three children in four years. Life was great. Career. Love. Family.

Then it happened. I fell into a deep dark pit and had no idea I had fallen into it. This was right around year eight as an attending that the proverbial ball dropped. I had three great children, three healthy pregnancies and a loving spouse but my life was not in balance. I injured my knee running and dealt with an undiagnosed injury despite MRI imaging, orthopedic visits, stacks of NSAIDS and multiple arthrocentesis procedures - the diagnosis was finally made in the operating room 1 year after the initial injury. By this time, my girth had increased, my clothing size had gone up and my body was incredibly deconditioned and atrophied. It was the inability to fit into my suit when I was getting ready to give a talk to the residents that shook me. I got a fitness coach and started to work on my self-care by honing my nutrition and working out 5-6 times per week for 30 minutes. After a few weeks, I noticed that I was a different person, a happier, more confident one.

During this time that my cryptic injury prevailed, I was showing all the signs of physician burnout but was completely unaware. It was happenstance that led me to focus on my fitness and nutrition; that focus then led to a realization that it was not normal to dread going into work each night to serve the patients that I trained so long and made so many sacrifices to care for. The transformation was so tremendous that I decided to become a fitness coach to help other busy women regain their mojos. This passion pursuit led to the establishment of my company, Fervently Fit with Charmaine, LLC.

In the five years that the company has been in existence, it has gone through an evolution (or two or three). I started out as a fitness and accountability coach, then I started to become interested in getting the word out about burnout. Over the years, I have been very open with my story in the hopes that hearing it will help others to overcome and thrive. Recall that I have a predilection for fear and fearlessness? Well, in the last two years, I have focused on facing my own fears head on and figuring out action steps and a way forward. My big fear is public speaking. In order to face this fear, I started to do live broadcasts on social media, put myself out there as a public speaker and started a podcast. In the fall of 2018, I got certified as a physician-coach in order to be able to hone the skills needed in order to help colleagues thrive in lieu of drowning in burnout.

Now, I do group coaching on resilience and burnout at conferences and professional meetings. In 2019, I will take on about 6 one-on-one clients on a very selective basis to guide them through career decision making, passion pursuit exploration, resilience tools, burnout troubleshooting, and entrepreneurial interests. In addition, my fitness coaching is currently limited to teaching MMA (mixed martial arts) inspired group fitness classes at professional meetings.

My goal is to pay it forward so that others don't get caught unaware and alone as I did. I hope to help colleagues and busy professional women to face fear and emerge victoriously.

Fear is all around us. The transformation of this energy force into fuel for forward progress is paramount. Be fearless.
Be strong. Be brave. Unleash your greatness.

CHAPTER 6: TRANSFORMATIVE

Dr. Hardin is a board-certified pediatrician with over 19 years of experience in outpatient and inpatient pediatrics. She completed her undergraduate studies in Biology at Talladega College in Alabama. Her medical school training was completed at Morehouse School of Medicine in Atlanta, Georgia, pediatric internship at the University of South Florida in Tampa, Florida and pediatric residency at Emory University in Atlanta, Georgia. Throughout Dr. Hardin's training, she has demonstrated academic excellence by graduating from college and medical school magna and cum laude respectively. She also achieved the top physician academic honor of induction into the Alpha Omega Alpha Honor Medical Society and is certified by the American Board of Pediatrics and American Board of Quality Assurance and Utilization Review Physicians in Health Care Quality and Management. She currently holds licenses to practice medicine in the states of Florida and Georgia.

Throughout her career, she has participated in various research and fellowship programs. While participating in the Minority Access to Research Careers Program as an undergraduate, she conducted breast cancer research at the University of Miami, which involved measuring the degree of aromatase

inhibition in the reduction of estrogen dependent breast tumors. She received a fellowship in Maternal and Child Health while matriculating at the Morehouse School of Medicine where she educated inner city families about the dangers of lead poisoning and studied new drug delivery systems during a fellowship at Mercer University Southern School of Pharmacy. One of her most challenging experiences while in medical school was working on the development of an AIDS vaccine through a fellowship with the Harvard AIDS Institute at the Dana Farber Cancer Center in Boston. As a National Health Service Corps scholar, she provided medical services to an underserved population in Gadsden, Alabama with the goal of increasing access to preventive care. She learned early on about the importance of being creative in her approach to healthcare and challenged the disparities leading to poor health through prevention, education, and research. She currently works in the role of Physician Advisor, where she assists physicians and hospitals with determining medical necessity. She also works as a telemedicine physician to help improve affordable access to health care.

Certified Coach with FASTer Way to Fat Loss®

My mission is to empower my clients to take control of their health and weight using cutting edge nutritional strategies, whole foods, and intentional exercise ultimately resulting in "Transformative" and sustainable weight loss.

As I reflect on my "transformative journey", it is evident to me from very early on that my passion is in preventative care. This influenced my choice to attend medical school at Morehouse School of Medicine as well as my decision to become a National Health Service Corps scholar. Both choices were instrumental in providing me with the necessary knowledge and tools needed to diagnose and treat potentially chronic diseases. Obesity is one of the most common chronic illnesses contributing to many preventable diseases including heart disease, stroke, diabetes, and certain types of cancer. At the age of 29 years, I can remember weighing in at 117 pounds. I did not exercise and could eat whenever, whatever, and as much as I wanted without gaining a single ounce. I felt invincible like most young adults. I don't have to tell you that this was a recipe for disaster!

Like many physicians, my focus was not on myself but on being a "Super-doctor", "Super-wife", "Supermom", and "Super" everything! My highest weight was 170 pounds, with a BMI of 30.1, firmly placing me into the obese category. Undoubtedly, this was a combination of stubborn post-baby weight, not eating the right foods nor exercising, and yes, those dreaded over-a-certain-age pounds! I also began to have high blood pressure and cholesterol. My energy level was also tanking as well as my self-esteem. Further complicating my "Superwoman" status was the diagnosis of an autoimmune illness along with an extremely low vitamin D level. So, more tiredness, fatigue, and joint pain! I had almost given up but the "Super" part of me, would not allow it. I realized that I had to do something to improve my health or risk suffering the consequences that I had spent so many years educating patients and their families about. I wanted to be present for those special milestones and moments with my husband and daughter as much as I could, so I started being more mindful of the way I lived my life.

In my quest to achieve and maintain a healthy weight and lifestyle, I tried several programs that just didn't work for me. They were either prohibitively expensive, required the purchase of too many additional products, or left me hangrily in starvation mode! I was able to lose some of the weight but it was usually short term which became very frustrating. I was beginning to realize that what I needed more was a lifestyle change to really make the difference. This was not an easy task for me. During college and medical school, I lived and survived on pizza, burgers, fries, and soda. I had really given up on finding something sustainable until I was introduced to the FASTer Way to Fat Loss. The program was created by Amanda Tress and is certified by the National Academy of Sports Medicine (NASM) and the Athletics and Fitness Association of America (AFAA). I watched the transformation of a friend not knowing which program she was doing until I decided to inquire. This was my introduction to the FASTer Way. I was hesitant and reluctant at first given my lack of success with other programs. However, in light of my age and new health concerns, I decided to give it a try and have never looked back.

It was a whirlwind at first as I was not well versed in

the program's nutritional strategies. I spent the first-round learning about the concepts of intermittent fasting, macro tracking, and carbohydrate cycling. Though modified due to painful knees, I incorporated more exercise with the second-round while learning how to weave it into my everyday activities. It became second nature to me even while being a busy physician mom, homeschool parent, wife, daughter to aging parents, and home-based business owner! After completing two coach led rounds for a total of 14 weeks, to my amazement I had lost 17 pounds, 11 inches, and two pant sizes while actually being able to EAT! I didn't have to unrealistically cut calories to for it to work for me. I knew that I had to find a way to share this with other women and men with similar weight struggles. So, I chose to deep dive into the program due to my success and after seeing the concepts work for so many others. What I learned was truly life changing. Contrary to what I thought was the right way to lose weight, i.e. not eating and exercising like crazy, I learned how to strategically eat real food and exercise in a way that worked for me and my metabolism. I don't stress about food or my weight anymore. I eat intuitively. Most importantly, the FASTer Way gave the control over food back to me which I feel is so important for sustainable weight loss. Thus, solidifying my desire to become a certified coach and giving me the ability to share the program with fellow physicians and my community.

As a coach, I provide instruction and guidance about the nutritional benefits of carbohydrate cycling, intermittent fasting, tracking macros, and intentional exercise. I help clients change their bodies into fat burning vessels of lean muscle by pairing the right exercise with the right nutrition at the right time. We consume the right amount of macronutrients (50% carbohydrates, 20% protein, and 30% healthy fats), during a 16:8 fasting schedule, with an intentional variation of carbohydrate intake so that we burn fat and build muscle with the goal of keeping our metabolism running smoothly and hormones functioning appropriately. We include whole foods, preferably gluten and dairy free without the primary focus being on calorie restriction but on providing the body with adequate fuel for optimal fat burning. My role as your coach is to guide you through the different strategies while providing daily instruction, feedback, accountability, and support to help you reach your goals. Guidance is key to balancing all three strategies simultaneously for the best outcome. My goal is to equip you with the necessary tools to not only take an active part in your transformation but also to empower you to maintain and continue incorporating the strategies into your everyday life.

Transforming your life is within reach. Allow me to bring the FASTer Way to Fat Loss online program to you which includes comprehensive preparatory training to make sure you are comfortable with the concepts, meal ideas, strategies for incorporating your taste preferences, password protected portal, daily workouts at the home, gym, low impact, beginner, and advanced levels, and daily accountability within the FASTer Way community. "Sometimes your only available transportation is a leap of faith."

-Margaret Shepard.

Yours truly in health and wellness,

Regina A. Hardin, MD

CHAPTER 7: PURPOSEFUL

Dr. Sonia Wright is a board-certified radiologist practicing in Minnesota. She is also a certified life coach with two distinct coaching niches. She is a life coach for physicians, doctors-in-training and pre-med students as well as a sexual counselor for women in midlife. When not interpreting radiology studies and coaching/counseling, Dr. Wright enjoys travel, theatre, dancing and being a mom. Her son is a sophomore at Stanford University and her daughter is a first grader.

I truly believe that life is meant to be lived in order to learn vital lessons, which in turn will help you to understand the reason for your existence. Everyone is put on this earth for a reason, a life purpose. These lessons, once learned, will help you to develop into the person necessary to execute your life purpose. This purpose allows you to make a difference in the world. Every person has a story which is unfolding, chapter by chapter, lesson by lesson, until their life's purpose becomes evident. Here is my story.

Chapter one: Childhood

My parents are from the Caribbean islands of Barbados and Jamaica. They immigrated to England to get their nursing training. I was born in England, but we immigrated to Canada soon after my birth. I spent the first five years of my life in a loving, supportive Caribbean community outside of Toronto. I have many fond memories of that time in my life. However, my parents felt the family's future was in the United States, so we moved to a small working-class town in Massachusetts in the early 1970's. My life dramatically changed when we moved to the United States. The extended Caribbean community that had nurtured me to this point in my life was gone. In addition, my parents' nursing degrees were not recognized in the United States, so they had to work two to three jobs to support the family. My siblings and I basically raised ourselves. Although my childhood was not easy, I learned some of the skills that would form the foundation for my life. Self-reliance, perseverance, love of learning, determination and mental toughness helped me to succeed. Being one of only a few black kids in the entire small town, I encountered my share of racism which fueled my need to excel academically. Since we were poor, I figured the only way out of this town was with a college scholarship. By the time I graduated high school, I was ranked second in my class. Life lesson: <u>Life is often not easy. What feels like adversity in the moment, often helps to forge your strongest character traits and lays the foundation for your future work.</u>

Chapter two: College

In 1984, I entered Stanford University on a full scholarship. I'm eternally grateful to Stanford University because they gave me an opportunity to obtain an incredible education that changed the course of my life. However, entering college was a difficult transition for me. The intersectionality of race, socioeconomic class and gender hit me hard at this elite institution. I felt like I did not belong on so many different levels. I did not understand it at the time, but it is a common experience for marginalized people. On top of that, the debate on Affirmative Action was coming to a head in our country. There was this unspoken, pervasive belief among many students at Stanford that minority students were "let in" and not necessarily academically qualified. I internalized that belief and it took me years to overcome it. At college graduation, I remember thinking that I was finished with institutions of higher education and would never return. Of course, I have to laugh now, as I did not know then that I had an additional 14 years of higher education/medical training ahead of me. Life Lesson: <u>Sometimes your purpose requires that you dive deep into uncomfortable places now, so you can assist others in the future.</u>

Chapter three: The path begins to be revealed

After graduation I moved up to Seattle with my fiancé where he pursued his master's degree in architecture. I did not have a defined career path. I worked for a health insurance company for a while and then became a financial counselor in a hospital. In 1991, we decided to move to England to live there for a year. We were married in England and eventually made our way back to the States by the end of 1992. I continued to work with medical financial accounts but was not very enthusiastic about this field. I loved talking to patients about their health challenges and was not as concerned about them paying their bills. I began volunteering in a homeless clinic. Through a lot of soul searching, I decided I wanted to become a doctor and work with the low-income patient population. However, I did not have the prerequisites courses for medical school.

In 1995, I enrolled at San Francisco State University (SFSU) to complete my post-baccalaureate premed course work. I loved my time at San Francisco State University. It is a vibrant campus with a diverse student population in the middle of San Francisco. This time around, I was aligned with my purpose of becoming a doctor. I excelled in my premed classwork and also took additional classes in anthropology and gender studies just for the fun of learning. I was an average of 10 years older than most students at SFSU and definitely had a different perspective on life. The SFSU students came from all different socioeconomic backgrounds and cultures, but many of these students did not have the educational opportunities and life experiences that I had enjoyed. I decided I wanted to give back to the students at SFSU, so I founded an organization called Students of Color in the Pre-Health Professions (SOCPHP). This organization encouraged kids from different backgrounds to consider careers in health care. I eventually led several different pre-health organizations on campus over the course of my time at SFSU. Life Lesson: <u>If you have been given many opportunities in life, you have a responsibility to reach out and help others. It's time to serve.</u>

Chapter four: Medical school

At the age of 32, ten years after completing my bachelor's degree, I matriculated at the University of California, San Francisco School of Medicine as a Regent Scholar, their highest academic honor. I had two goals when I started medical school: first to become a physician and second to be a mother. My son Julien was born a year later during the first week of my second year, which I split into two years. Becoming a mother was one of the best decisions I have ever made in my life, but also one of the hardest. I had a C-section and went back to classes two weeks after Julien was born. In addition, my baby could not breastfeed, so I had to pump every three hours around the clock to keep up my milk supply. A year into it all, I was exhausted and dealing with postpartum issues. It was the first time in my life that I realized I could not do it all. I needed to listen to my body and heal my spirit. I did a radiology research project to give myself time to heal before going on the wards. This turned out to be a great decision as I grew to love radiology. By the end of my third year, I knew I wanted to pursue a career in Diagnostic Radiology. I worked hard in my third and fourth year and eventually matched in Diagnostic Radiology at the Mayo Clinic. Life Lesson: <u>Listen to your body and soul. Take the time to rest and replenish when necessary.</u>

Chapter five: Starting Over

My time at the Mayo Clinic was a turning point in my life. Mayo's commitment to excellence, patient care, and customer service had a profound impact upon how I function even today as a radiologist and as an entrepreneur. However, it was also one of the most difficult times in my life. I struggled to thrive in the very conservative environment of Rochester, MN. In addition, my marriage fell apart and we divorced. I had to start over from scratch while juggling the demands of a challenging radiology residency and the responsibilities of being a divorced parent. It was also during this time that I came out as queer. I knew I needed help to get through this time and decided to look into life coaching. I signed up for life coaching with a Franciscan nun called Sister Linda Wieser. She was literally an angel sent from heaven. Sister Linda was my guide who accompanied me through the remainder of my residency and my fellowship.

Life coaching gave me the tools to address any problem that I encountered. I learned that situations are neutral, it is our thoughts about the situation and our struggle to change the circumstances which cause so much unnecessary pain. About 50% of the time, we are going to experience negative emotions and that is actually not a problem. If we can accept the situation, then we can learn how to reframe our ideas and ultimately lead to new actions and new results. I learned that nothing has gone wrong in life. It all unfolds exactly as it should. I also learned there is nothing innately wrong with us. We are not damaged or need to be fixed. We are all perfectly imperfect. Life Lesson: <u>Resistance causes much pain in life. Acceptance of circumstances and self ultimately lead to peace. From a place of peace, your life purpose can be revealed.</u>

Chapter six: My life purpose revealed

Over the last 10 years, I have continued on my personal journey of growth and discovery, reflecting upon my purpose in life. When I turned 50, I started asking myself "how can I continue to be of service during the second half of my life?" I decided to shift gears and become a life coach while continuing my job as a radiologist. From 2016-2018, I completed two life coaching training programs and began offering my services to the medical community. For the last six years, I have been mentoring pre-med students from the local universities' diversity pre-med programs. I had been advising them on the requirements for medical school, but I felt that was not enough. I wanted to equip them with the skills necessary to really thrive in medical school. I developed a program to coach my pre-med students on believing in themselves, self-care, time management, goal setting and mental resilience. At the same time, I looked around at my physician colleagues and saw that many were struggling with burnout and desperately needed to develop similar skills. So, I began offering life coaching to physicians as well.

In addition to offering life coaching to medical professionals, doctors in training and premed students, I also offer life coaching to the general public, which inadvertently led to the development of my second niche. Many of my clients are women in midlife (age 40-60+) struggling with health concerns, body image, menopause and relationship/intimacy issues. Once I gained my clients trust, they felt comfortable enough to discuss specific problems related to relationships and sexual intimacy. They often mentioned they needed to discuss the issue with someone but did not know who could help them. I wanted to be that person whom they could confide in, but I needed more training. So, in April of 2018, I enrolled in a 12-month certificate program in Sexual Counseling at the University of Michigan, School of Social Work.

During this last year, I have been developing my 12-week Sex Coaching Program. I kept asking myself, "what are the best services that I could provide my clients?" I decided to combine my medical knowledge, sexual counseling training and my life coaching skills to provide a unique holistic program to address my clients' sexual and health concerns.

The objectives of my program are to...

- Help you realize whatever issues you are dealing with now are completely normal in a woman's life and can be improved. Let's work on it together!

- Help you get to a place of self-love and body acceptance, so you can create the sex life of your dreams. Your body is incredible!
- Help you become comfortable with and enjoy your own sexuality. You have the right to a fabulous sex life!
- Help you increase sexual intimacy with your partner- no matter what emotional or medical issues have developed over time. Sexual intimacy can be improved!
- Help you work on low desire/libido issues. Many factors influence desire, but you can improve it!
- Help you identify how your health issues or that of your partner may be impeding sex and help you create modifications to enjoy sex. Don't limit yourself to a narrow definition of sex!
- Help you understand how your body changes with perimenopause and menopause. Perimenopausal and postmenopausal sex can be the best sex of your life!

- Help you explore any sexual interests you may have in a safe and nonjudgmental environment. You deserve to be happy!

This journey to living my life on purpose continues to unfold. As I enter this next chapter in my life's journey, I'm curious to see how I will grow and change and most importantly, how I can continue to contribute and serve. I'm grateful for all the experiences I've had in my life so far because they have made me the woman, mother, doctor, coach and mentor that I am today. If I can be of service to you, please feel free to contact me.

CHAPTER 8: PRIORITIZER

Dr. Jattu Senesie is a board-certified obstetrician-gynecologist and native of the Washington DC metropolitan area. She is an alumna of the University of Maryland Baltimore County where she graduated magna cum laude with a degree in Biological Sciences. Her medical training took her to Emory University School of Medicine in Atlanta, GA. There she obtained her medical degree and completed her residency training in the Department of Gynecology and Obstetrics. Dr Senesie returned to the DC area after training and spent six years in a private obstetrics and gynecology practice in Maryland.

Dr. Senesie retired from clinical practice in 2010 in an attempt to find a balance between maintaining her own sense of well-being and living a life of service. Since leaving clinical medicine, she has become a certified success coach and founded her business: Essence of Strength. She is dedicated to helping early career healthcare professionals be as intentional about their sense of satisfaction as they are about their success so they can fulfill their potential inside and outside the clinical setting.

It is a strange phenomenon to be a high achieving professional who knows you have accomplished your intended goals and still feel like you haven't fulfilled your potential. There are conflicting emotions of feeling ungrateful for the life you have and knowing that you have more to give to the world than you currently do. That is the dilemma I encountered during my time in practice as an obstetrician-gynecologist.

My journey through this existential crisis into a space where I feel genuinely satisfied with the success, I have achieved brought me to my work as a coach for early career physicians. My story taught me that the process of becoming a good clinician doesn't necessarily yield the skillset that helps maintain fulfillment as a human being. What is essential for a sustained sense of satisfaction within any circumstance is honoring one's own priorities.

At the ripe old age of twelve, I decided to become an obstetrician-gynecologist. My aptitude in science and strong desire to help others seemed to lend itself quite nicely to being a physician. Coupling that with my fascination with anatomy, maternal-fetal physiology and reproductive endocrinology made specializing in women's reproductive health a no-brainer for me. Yes, that is where my mind was as a pre-teen.

My priorities at that time were centered around getting into a good college that would set me up for a smooth journey along the well-structured path of medical training. Over the next two decades, there was never a point when I veered off the traditional course to becoming a board-certified ob/gyn. My personal priorities aligned well with those of the system for producing competent physicians. I got the grades and passed the exams to keep me moving forward from ambitious middle schooler to attending physician. The unspoken assumption was that my priorities would continue to align with those of the healthcare system and thus bring my desired sense of satisfaction along with success.

There were definitely times during medical training when I questioned whether the whole process was going to be worth it in the end. I was always reassured that whatever challenge I was currently facing was not reflective of what my real life as a doctor would be. If my priorities were not being honored in the moment, it was only temporary. It would pass and the next thing would be better.

Memorizing and regurgitating facts during the first two years of med school was a necessary evil to prepare me for the excitement of seeing patients on the hospital wards. Taking care of asthmatic kids and hypertensive men was a required part of the process before I got to focus on women's health. Being short-handed and sleep-deprived for much of residency was a brief inconvenience in comparison to the autonomy of being an attending physician.

Every challenge offered the promise of a better future. In reality, it was never really good, even when it was better. The more professional milestones I achieved, the less my life seemed like one that would be fulfilling to me in the long term. Still, I kept holding out hope. Preparing for and passing my oral board examination was supposed to be the final challenge on my path to a satisfied life as an ob/gyn. Once I passed that barrier, my life inside and outside of work was going to reflect my priorities. There would be perfect alignment of my sense of satisfaction and my external success.

You can imagine my dismay at passing my oral boards, looking around at my life and thinking, "This is as good as it gets?!" It was overwhelming to realize I didn't like the life I had spent twenty years developing by strictly following what seemed like a foolproof plan. When being a good clinician who passed my certification exams on the first try didn't bring me fulfillment, I was too embarrassed to admit it to anyone except a mental health professional.

Therapy gave me two big insights. First, I had been conditioned over the course of my medical training into the default setting of deferring my preferences and priorities. This led me to a life with almost no traces of my priorities once training was complete. I no longer really knew what was important to me separate from what was important to the establishment. Second, I was so burnt out from living my life in deference to other people's priorities I needed a break before I planned how to fix it.

Those realizations prompted my one-hundred-day sabbatical from practice. This was my first step away from the traditional physician career path. No doctor

I knew ever took time off except for birth or death of a family member. Personal illness didn't even get you a sick day when your job was to be the healer.

I naively thought I would be fixed after my time off because I had finally acknowledged that I wanted to prioritize my quality of life. My new clear head did allow me to design strategies to modify my clinic schedule, home location and practice base in ways meant to provide an environment for me to thrive inside and outside of work. Unfortunately, thriving did not occur because I was using what I didn't like as the catalyst for change instead of starting with what I valued.

As you might imagine, that approach led to another case of burnout in only two more years. The tension of seeing how what I prioritized wasn't reflected in my life was less sustainable after my sabbatical. Knowing what my priorities were without knowing how to honor them in a practical way was worse than being unaware. Being very busy and productive was not allowing me to make the most of my gifts in a way that was fulfilling to me. Ironically, I decided to leave the career I had spent my whole life training to do in order to achieve my full potential.

Like many physicians seeking a change, I initially thought more and different training and education was what I needed. Maybe another degree would tap into that well of satisfaction that had thus far eluded me. After determining that wasn't the right move for me, I decided that rejecting traditional systems and structure was going to be the answer. The healthcare industrial complex had set me on a path to becoming a pathological altruist. I wanted to get outside the box in order to thrive.

My priorities didn't align with the systems of which I had been apart, so clearly systems must have been my enemy. Except, they weren't. Historically, systems and structure are what aided my success. I simply hadn't learned how to remain true to my priorities within those systems so I could feel satisfied. What I needed was unconventional thinking applied to my circumstances without tossing systematic approaches away.

Once I determined I needed some structure for being as intentional about satisfaction as I had been about success, I hired a coach. The first three nonclinical years on my own cobbling together strategies and skills gave me new experiences that still weren't fulfilling to me. Once the novelty wore off, I found myself falling back into disillusionment that I wasn't fulfilling my potential and respecting my priorities. Working with my coach, I used a system based on my personal priorities to help me find satisfaction with success. Rather than picking strategies that seemed like they would work for someone like me, I developed personalized strategies based on what mattered most to me.

Going through that process was so enlightening for me I realized how useful it would have been during my time in clinical medicine. I learned I could honor my priorities and those of others at the same time in a way that left us all satisfied. Most importantly, I came to accept that any situation where I was not able to prioritize what was important to me was likely not the right fit for me or them.

Being coached also helped me recognize how I could use my knowledge and experience as a clinician to fulfill my potential away from the bedside. Sharing with my fellow physicians the system, structure and tools I learned for being satisfied was my new mission. Early career physicians who were disillusioned didn't need to resign themselves to misery until retirement or leave clinical medicine altogether like I did. Instead, they could learn how to thrive by implementing strategies that respected their priorities and allowed them to achieve their goals inside or outside of the clinical space.

Coaching as my second career has been so fulfilling for me. People often question whether I feel like all those years in medical training and practice were wasted. On the contrary, I feel like coaching physicians is a wonderful way to use my interests, skills and experience to impact the overall healthcare system in a positive way. That ambitious and altruistic twelve-year-old would be proud to help her fellow healers be well.

CHAPTER 9: CHANGER

Dr. Vanessa Jeffers is a native New Yorker, born and raised in the borough of Brooklyn. Board certified in Internal Medicine, she received her Bachelor of Arts Degree from Cornell University, and was awarded her Doctor of Medicine Degree from New York Medical College. In 1992, Dr. Jeffers completed her Residency training at Westchester Medical Center, where she was the first African American appointed to serve as Chief Medical Resident in the Department of Medicine and was also inducted into the Alpha Omega Alpha Medical Honor Society.

With a desire to give back, her first job out of residency was as an Internist at The Peekskill Area Health Center in Peekskill, New York. The following year, Dr. Jeffers joined the Department of Internal Medicine at The Brooklyn Hospital Center as a full time Attending. While there, she served as the Medical Director for Ambulatory Care and as Co-Chief of General Internal Medicine. She also served on the Hospital Center's Medical Board and numerous other committees. In 2005, she left to establish her private practice in the Fort Greene section of Brooklyn.

In 2017, Dr. Jeffers left private practice, coming full circle, and is presently in practice at a family health center in Bedford-Stuyvesant, continuing to serve the patients of the borough in which she resides. Always looking for ways to create health and not just manage disease, Dr. Jeffers also became a Certified Health and Wellness Coach in 2012. Using a successful healthy lifestyle program, she empowers her patients to transform their health. In 2017, Dr. Jeffers became a co-author of the best seller, Thinking About Quitting Medicine?, a collaborative labor of love and therapy with twelve other doctors to help uplift their medical colleagues. When she's not treating patients in the office, or speaking in the community, she's assisting other physicians and health professionals on their personal health journey and /or enhancing their practices to also coach patients toward better health. Helping others achieve optimal health is her passion.

If you were to ask my mother, she would say that I've always wanted to be a doctor. And it's probably true. Growing up, my father worked hard in a knitwear manufacturing factory. Having no health insurance and paying out of pocket for medical care, one becomes keenly aware of disparities in access to and quality of healthcare, even as a child. As I recall, my dream to help others be well and come back to my neighborhood to practice definitely started to come together in junior high and high school. A product of New York City public schools, I was in AP classes and then pre-med at Cornell University. (If I hadn't become a physician, I probably would have become a teacher. A science teacher.) Medical School at New York Medical College and then Residency training in Internal Medicine at Westchester Medical Center was part of my journey to being the board certified Internist I am today. Over the course of my career, like other physicians, I spent the majority of my day diagnosing and treating diseases, but now, I also help CREATE health. I'm a Change Agent.

"But Dr. Jeffers, she weighs MORE than I do!" This was a patient's response almost twenty years ago. We had agreed her weight was something we wanted to work on. Something she wanted to work on. Something to help improve her blood pressure, and I was just trying to figure out why she was refusing to return to the nutritionist I had referred her to. Someone I thought could help her. And her answer was, "But Dr. Jeffers, she weighs MORE than I do!" Period. It reminded me of that old saying, "Do as I say, not as I do." Another Aha moment. There had been others. Patients were watching us.

I didn't set out to become a health and wellness coach or be the go-to physician on weight loss. It sort of just happened. I simply started out trying to help my patients. I can't speak for my colleagues, but it was obvious to me that preventive medicine was important. I guess that's the Internist in me. Looking at my patient population, largely bread and butter internal medicine, I saw a lot of hypertension, diabetes, and cardiovascular disease. At the same time, I had a lot of overweight and obese patients. No one was talking about an "obesity epidemic" back then, but we knew that it was a modifiable risk factor that could lead to many other chronic illnesses. I started thinking. So, what if we really worked on the weight? Starting mediations and increasing medications, like pills and insulin, didn't seem to be enough. I thought, if we REALLY worked on the weight, it could make a difference.

My training in internal medicine didn't focus on

weight loss or weight management. The focus of our education and training is larger and broader and covers all the things physicians must know to diagnose and treat illness. As it should. But I knew about the science of weight loss. Patients often asked me how I maintained my weight, saying "Dr. Jeffers, you always weigh the same". Well that's because I know diets don't work and overtime, I had developed healthy habits, which became a lifestyle that I have maintained for years. Now, it's like second nature. But it wasn't always like that. Like most women, I've been on my share of diets when I was younger and put on the "freshman 15" during college. Patients wanted to know what I ate, did I exercise, and in other words, what were my habits to maintain a healthy lifestyle. More and more I realized, that just as the nutritionist was a model of poor health, that my patients saw me as a model of good health. As physicians, we are uniquely positioned to influence the behaviors of our patients. Think about it. How many times have you scratched your head and wondered to yourself, "with all we know about lung cancer, how can they still smoke?" when we see that pulmonologist or respiratory therapist in back of the hospital smoking a cigarette. It's the same thing with our patients. Or consider this, who would go to a hair stylist for service, if their hair was unkempt and always looked as if they just rolled out of bed? Until that time, it had never occurred to me, that in taking care of myself, during the course of my everyday work, I was sending a message about being healthy without saying a word. I had to figure out a way to share what I knew. No longer would the simple phrase, "eat less and move more", with a bunch of handouts, one including the food pyramid, be enough. My patients deserved better. I had to figure out a way to break it down. I needed to break down the habits and lifestyle I learned for myself, into something structured and simple for others to follow.

First, I had to expand my knowledge in this area. In 2005, I took a course in Physician Medical Weight Loss and began helping patients in my Internal Medicine practice. We started talking about weight and BMI. I know, what a concept. It became sort of like a fifth or sixth vital sign. I learned that many patients did not consider themselves “overweight” or “obese”, and therefore did not consider themselves at risk for hypertension, diabetes and cardiovascular disease which is largely preventable. One patient thanked me for being honest. Crying, she said no doctor had ever told explained it to her and she was ready to make a change.

My extra training was comprehensive, but in my opinion, did not fully address behavioral modification, which should be a cornerstone of any weight loss or weight maintenance program. It’s what builds healthy habits and increases the chance of lifelong success. So, I didn’t stop there, but at the same time, I wasn’t trying to recreate the wheel. My desire to find programs and tools to truly help patients create health lead me to eventually become a Certified Health Coach in 2012. After much research, I finally found a comprehensive program that I could easily share with my patients. It essentially guided them as they developed the healthy habits I had developed. It wasn’t some fad diet. It was physician-led, evidence-based, and clinically proven, with a long track record. Start-up cost was low, and it was easy to implement. I could understand the science and why it worked. Becoming a part of a national organization of independent Health Coaches which included other physicians and health professionals who "get it" was exactly what I was searching for. Instead of just treating disease, I was actually helping patients create health. Years later, my patients continue to have great results. Whether it is 10 pounds or 100 pounds, less knee pain or back pain, lower blood pressure or improved HgbA1C and not having to start medication, I love it!

As a health and wellness coach, whether my client is a physician, other health professional, or patient within or outside my practice, I work closely with them, one on one, as a guide on a journey to better health. The journey is never just about weight, although for most, that's where it starts. We begin with a discussion about what they would like to accomplish, and what is their current state of health. In my experience, there are 6 significant factors that contribute to overall physical health. So, to get a good idea of their daily habits, we explore how they are doing in the areas of hydration, motion, sleep, stress, weight, and eating habits. Most importantly, we identify their main motivation for change, their WHY. Using a comprehensive approach, clients are empowered to transform their health. From day one, they become a part of a wellness community. There is a structured meal plan with written and online guides, and multiple levels of support including coaching calls, motivational messages, webinars, interactive private social media groups to name a few. Clients learn portion control, what to eat and when. Once engaged, day by day, healthy habits are formed and a foundation for transformation is built, creating a sustainable lifestyle.

Coaching physicians in this lifestyle transformation and empowering them to serve as models of good health has been particularly rewarding. I've enjoyed seeing them become healthier. Doctors are people too, and most are no different than the general public when it comes to weight. Although caring for patients in various specialties, many are overweight and obese like their patients, and despite a science background, are reaching for the latest fad diets, or doing the same thing they've always done and expecting a different result like everyone else. As a busy physician myself, I know what it's like and I know what getting healthy takes. As a physician, you are not looking for complicated and time consuming. You are looking for simple and easy to incorporate into your day, whether you are rounding on the wards, seeing patients in the office or in and out of the operating room. Because we do better in community and with accountability, a coach helps. You don't have time to go to meetings, so having access to a coach using modalities like video chat, and text, or a simple phone call, works for you. All without judgement. My physician clients have done wonderfully on this program.

In my role as a practice wellness consultant, I've also enjoyed helping many physicians successfully and seamlessly incorporate this program into their practices. Mind you, not all started as weight loss or wellness clients, but many have. Again, using one on one coaching, free training and the support of a community of physicians and other health professionals, I help them set up an effective wellness center in their practice. I like the fact that the program is physician led. As a physician, it was important that my program was evidence- based and clinically proven. This business model isn't for everyone, but it fit what I was looking for and has allowed me to make a difference in the lives of others. For physicians or health professionals not looking to recreate the wheel, but looking for something with turnkey implementation, low basic start-up cost, no inventory and ancillary income, this could be for you and I would be honored to help.

I believe my purpose is to be a Change Agent in the area of health and wellness, and I feel especially drawn to helping other physicians transform their lifestyles; thereby empowering them to serve as models of health. This could create a ripple effect which will improve the health of their family members, neighbors, church family, patients and the larger community.

Imagine if all physicians and health professionals were models of good health. Imagine the impact that would have on our healthcare system. Imagine the impact it would have on the health of our patients, their families, and the communities in which we practice. Our patients are indeed watching us and we are model of health, good or bad, whether we think we are or not. Imagine. We all can be Change Agents.

CHAPTER 10: ALIGNED

Dr. Stiegler is a physician entrepreneur who helps other physicians achieve the professional and business success that is aligned with their personal values. A Harvard-trained internationally recognized expert, she has career experience in academic medicine, private practice, nonprofit organizations, industry, and nonmedical business ventures. A seasoned speaker, she has presented around the globe (even with 2 Nobel laureates!) on behavioral science, leadership, and career acceleration. She has grown numerous ideas to highly profitable companies and leverages this experience as a career strategy and business coach for doctors.

That's my bio. But here's what you really should know about me:

- I broke my spine during residency. It was so bad, there was a time I thought I would never graduate. (But I did.)
- Two years later I founded a maternity athletic apparel company. This was the beginning of

10+ years of digital marketing experience, self-taught.

- I was having a really successful academic career at the same time. I was incredibly focused on career strategy, productivity, and professional development.
- My husband was diagnosed with cancer.
- I dropped everything and learned some painful and powerful lessons about how I had been (mis)aligning my efforts with what mattered the most to me.
- I sold my company.
- I said no to everything for 18 months. Everything.
- With a new perspective, I reinvented my career and launched 4 successful brands in a single year.
- Colleagues asked me about each of these phases in my life, and I've been sharing what I learned ever since.

How does all of this fit with the concept of alignment?

My definition of success isn't based on typical business metrics. Instead, I help physicians earn money doing more of what they love, and less of what they don't. Although my clients have diverse backgrounds and goals, they are all seeking to align the way they spend their time and energy with what actually matters to them the most. By combining classic business principles with modern tactics and digital strategy, I've helped hundreds of doctors reclaim the intentionally aligned life they deserve – one with autonomy, purpose, joy, and fulfillment. My physician clients launch their dream businesses, grow their practices, make their side gigs profitable, and fast-track academic advancement. The nature of the goal doesn't matter – these strategies always work.

Medical training systematically extinguishes alignment with one's values. Because the needs of others always outrank personal needs or needs of cherished family and friends, physicians are in a never-ending conflict between their work obligations and their values. For example, most people value dependability. This is why a physician will have to be practically dead to take a day off. Patients and colleagues know that physician is unwaveringly dependable. But on the other hand, that physician's children don't have a dependable parent. The spouse doesn't have a dependable partner. The physician's body cannot depend upon the mind to make decisions that are healthy and self-nurturing. So, this life isn't truly aligned with the value of dependability at all. An aligned life is a balanced, happy, successful life. An aligned career feels like freedom and focus instead of feeling stuck and overwhelmed. An aligned strategy gets results instead of burnout.

In 2009, I became pregnant with my first child. Before medicine, I was a personal trainer, and while it wasn't my job anymore, I still loved fitness. Pregnancy changes things, and I, like many women, experienced a wildly changing dynamic with my body and my health. It's a longer story than I can fit into this chapter, but I got the inspiration to start a company for high-end athletic maternity apparel. (At the time, there was a big void in the market, or I probably would have simply shopped instead of launching my own business!) LA was a great place to be in this regard, because all of our factory and vendor needs were downtown – pattern design, fabric sourcing, cut and sew, etc. And so, before the rise of the instant website era, we built a retail business that we sold exclusively online. It was profitable from the first year and pulled in over 6 figures annually with customers around the globe. We used social media and organic marketing strategies to grow the company, learning as we went. Mostly on a whim, I decided to also establish an online presence for my academic self – what I would call my 'professional brand' today. I had a website with a blog that was focused on my interests and research, and I had a professional Twitter account. At first, no one was reading my blog and my professional community on social media was small. Then suddenly, my academic career exploded with international invitations and connections that I'm convinced would never have come to be without the power of the internet.

Perhaps like you, I experienced a considerable amount of 'mission creep' as my career progressed. I had more and more speaking engagements, more and more national and international travel, more and more committees and meetings. These were all good opportunities, and yet, as they continued to build, they spilled over into an all-consuming list of things I 'had to do' at the expense of the way I wanted to live. Maybe you can relate. I thought I was doing a pretty good job of 'saying no' to extraneous things, but I was forced to take a comprehensive look at everything I was doing when my husband was diagnosed with cancer. The list was long. I'm not sure I realized I had been hanging out in that denial zone, but when I dropped everything to focus 100% on family, it became clear.

Without a deliberate and aligned strategy, reality goes something like this:

Physicians like you have invested tremendous time, energy, and money into their careers. Yet, far too many are feeling bored, undervalued, invisible, or burned out. They're working a LOT, but not getting the opportunities to do the work they want most. In hopes of being eventually tapped for the roles they want, these doctors end up saying 'yes' to everything and everyone (except to themselves, and often, to their families). To fill their emotional cups just a bit, doctors are increasingly looking to entrepreneurial or side ventures that they really enjoy, despite having almost no free time and insufficient knowledge about business. But in a desperate bid to make that fulfilling work actually profitable, they overstretch and are at the brink of exhaustion, juggling a million balls and feeling powerless to stop. This is what I call 'the denial zone' – it's the end of the rope and it's totally unsustainable.

This is a paradigm that many of you are probably living – doing a less-than-best job at a million things, and while accomplishing a lot, getting little joy from it. Tack on the guilt that many feel from knowing we could have done it better. This is a bad deal for everyone. It's a bad deal for you, of course, but it is also a bad deal for your boss, your clients/patients/customers, and your colleagues who'd actually like to take over a few of your projects! (Had you thought about it that way?)

When we are constantly in fight-or-flight mode, we don't have the wherewithal to strategize or see the big picture; we are just trying to get through each day. A key part of creating an intentionally aligned career is breaking that cycle. We do that in a variety of ways, including the ruthless editing out and deliberate quitting of good – yes, good – activities. Good activities that are worthwhile, have merit, and are simply not the very best for you, specifically. This provides new opportunities for others, and often can open doors for them to move ahead in their careers, while freeing you to focus on what you do best and what you love most so that you can give your best attention, most energy, and do your best work. This is a totally different way of working – it's a paradigm of enthusiasm and joy instead of exhaustion.

Here's what I learned (both for my apparel company, and for my professional career):

1. Communication of your value is the key to success. Being able to offer something of high value is a requisite, but it is simply not enough. You've simply got to be able to describe your expert mojo in a way that is both clear and memorable. People have to know what they're going to get when they hire you, buy from you, tap you for a leadership role, ask you

to speak, etc. And, they have to be able to tell other people about it in a way that connects you to the benefits you bring to the table. Spoiler Alert – most people (especially doctors) are really bad at this. But it can be learned!

2. Visibility is essential. Never assume people know you exist. Never assume people are aware of your work or accomplishments. Most of the time, they aren't. Spoiler Alert – most doctors are really bad at this too! A little strategic effort here goes a very long way in terms of establishing credibility and a reputation for expertise.

3. If you understand how to use 1 and 2, you will flip the script. You'll be in the driver's seat, with more control, choices, negotiating power, and financial freedom than you've experienced before. And with that autonomy, you can make decisions to align your work with your most cherished values. You will be empowered to say yes to things you want to do and fearlessly decline the things you don't. You'll become like a magnet for the opportunities you desire, and you'll have the confidence to take risks and leave traditional expectations in the dust.

So, I offer a variety of programs, including The Social Prescription, The Branding Prescription, and The Speaking Prescription, as well as TransforMD Mastery events. These programs focus on just what they say – how to use social media, how to establish an effective brand, how to get paid as a professional speaker, and how to transform your chaotic life into an aligned life.

Why do my clients invest in my programs? Because while there is free information all over the internet on just about every topic imaginable, my clients want physician-centric approaches from someone just like them. Physicians looking to build professional visibility and grow entrepreneurial endeavors are a specific niche. What works in external industry (speaking, marketing, blogging) doesn't necessarily translate for us. It isn't always obvious how to apply branding, marketing, and other online strategy to a professional medical career (whether traditional or not). My clients don't want to have to waste time and effort doing their own trial-and-error vetting of sources or get stitched together information in a piecemeal way. They want an approach that is complete, in the right sequence, and includes the unique considerations many physicians face in life and at work.

And, they want to make bold changes with confidence, so they can live an aligned life with more balance, less stress, and deep purpose. I deliver practical strategies and clear action plans to create the right success opportunities. I help busy doctors rediscover and focus on what's truly important. The desired results are different for everyone, of course, but the prescription is the same.

ACKNOWLEDGMENTS AND CONTACT INFO

The docs of this book would like to thank their families, friends and colleagues who have supported them at all levels of their lives and careers.

We would like to thank the editors, graphic designers, marketing specialists and publishers with Swiner Publishing Company for helping us with this best-selling book.

And, most of all, we'd like to thank the readers, current and future, for your support.

With love,

All of us ☺

Here's how to get in contact with the authors--

Dr. Swiner:

Email: cnswiner@gmail.com

Website: docswiner.com

To schedule: calendly.com/docswiner

Social media: @docswiner on Facebook, Instagram, Twitter and LinkedIn

Blog: docswiner.blog

Subscription box info: superwomansurvivalkit.com and @thesuperwomansurvivalkit on Instagram

Dr. Ajmani:

Email: yoga.sheetal@gmail.com

Website: linktr.ee/sheetalajmanimd

Social media: @sheetalajmanimd on Facebook

Dr. Hammerstedt: 208.917.1090

Email: Heather@wholisthealth.com

Website: www.wholisthealth.com

Social media: @wholisthealth on Instagram, Twitter

www.facebook.com/wholisthealth

www.facebook.com/groups/hammerstedthealthand wellness

Dr. Senesie:

Email : jattu@essenceofstrength.com

Website: essenceofstrength.com

Social media:

FB: Essence of Strength with Dr Jattu Senesie

Instagram: @dressenceofstrength

Twitter: @EssenceStrength

Dr. Stiegler:

Email: Marjorie@marjoriestieglermd.com

Website: www. marjoriestieglermd.com

Social media: @DrMStiegler on Facebook and Twitter

Dr. Clairborne:

Website: www.DrMaiysha.com

www.StressFreeMomMD.com

www.NextLevelPhysicians.com

Social Media:

Facebook: https://www.facebook.com/DrMaiysha/

Instagram: @DrMaiysha

Dr. Jeffers:

Email: VanessaJeffersMD@gmail.com

To schedule: www.calendly.com/DrVanessaMD

Website: www.DrVanessaMD.com

Social Media: @DrVanessaMD on Twitter, Instagram

Facebook: https://facebook.com/DrVanessaMD (Living In Better Health With Dr. Vanessa Jeffers)

Dr. Wright:

Website: www.hopewelllifecoaching.com

www.themidlifesexcoach.com

Drsonia@themidlifesexcoach.com

Dr. Hardin:

Website: https://www.fasterwaycoach.com/#ReginaHardin

Social media:

https://www.facebook.com/regina.a.hardin

https://www.facebook.com/ReginaHardinMD/

Instagram: @regina.allen.hardin

Dr. Gregory:

Email:

Charmaine@ferventlyfitwithcharmaine.com

info@fearlessfreedomwithdrg.com

Website: www.ferventlyfitwithcharmaine.com

Dr. Watkins:

Website: www.latanjawatkins.com

Social media:

Facebook:
https://www.facebook.com/thephysicianburnoutco
ach

Instagram: @the_physician_burnout_coach

Made in the USA
Columbia, SC
16 June 2019